P9-CRQ-327

FAIR ROSAMOND.

A

DREAM OF FAIR WOMEN

BY

ALFRED TENNYSON

ILLUSTRATED

BOSTON
JAMES R. OSGOOD AND COMPANY

Copyright, 1880,

JAMES R. OSGOOD AND COMPANY.

All Rights Reserved.

University Press, Cambridge:

JOHN WILSON AND SON.

LIST OF ILLUSTRATIONS.

[Drawn and engraved under the supervision of A. V. S. Anthony.]

List of Illustrations.

A DREAM OF FAIR WOMEN.

A DREAM OF FAIR WOMEN.

I READ, before my eyelids dropt their shade,
  "*The Legend of Good Women*," long ago
Sung by the morning star of song, who made
  His music heard below;

Dan Chaucer, the first warbler, whose sweet breath
  Preluded those melodious bursts, that fill
The spacious times of great Elizabeth
  With sounds that echo still.

CHAUCER AND THE ELIZABETHAN POETS.

And, for a while, the knowledge of his art

    Held me above the subject, as strong gales

Hold swollen clouds from raining, tho' my heart,

    Brimful of those wild tales,

Charged both mine eyes with tears. In every land

   I saw, wherever light illumineth,

Beauty and anguish walking hand in hand

   The downward slope to death.

Those far-renowned brides of ancient song

   Peopled the hollow dark, like burning stars,

And I heard sounds of insult, shame, and wrong,

   And trumpets blown for wars;

And clattering flints batter'd with clanging hoofs:

   And I saw crowds in column'd sanctuaries;

And forms that pass'd at windows and on roofs

   Of marble palaces;

Corpses across the threshold; heroes tall

   Dislodging pinnacle and parapet

Upon the tortoise creeping to the wall;

Lances in ambush set;

And high shrine-doors burst thro' with heated blasts

That run before the fluttering tongues of fire;

White surf wind-scatter'd over sails and masts,

And ever climbing higher:

Squadrons and squares of men in brazen plates,

    Scaffolds, still sheets of water, divers woes,

Ranges of glimmering vaults with iron grates,

    And hush'd seraglios.

So shape chased shape as swift as, when to land

    Bluster the winds and tides the self-same way,

Crisp foam-flakes scud along the level sand,

    Torn from the fringe of spray.

I started once, or seem'd to start in pain,

    Resolved on noble things, and strove to speak,

As when a great thought strikes along the brain,

    And flushes all the cheek.

And once my arm was lifted to hew down

    A cavalier from off his saddle-bow,

That bore a lady from a leaguer'd town;
   And then, I know not how,

All those sharp fancies, by down-lapsing thought
   Stream'd onward, lost their edges, and did creep
Roll'd on each other, rounded, smooth'd, and brought
   Into the gulfs of sleep.

At last methought that I had wander'd far
   In an old wood: fresh-wash'd in coolest dew,
The maiden splendors of the morning star
   Shook in the steadfast blue.

Enormous elmtree-boles did stoop and lean
   Upon the dusky brushwood underneath
Their broad curved branches, fledged with clearest green,
   New from its silken sheath.

The dim red morn had died, her journey done,

And with dead lips smiled at the twilight plain,

Half-fall'n across the threshold of the sun,
   Never to rise again.

There was no motion in the dumb dead air,
   Not any song of bird or sound of rill;
Gross darkness of the inner sepulchre
   Is not so deadly still

As that wide forest. Growths of jasmine turn'd

    Their humid arms festooning tree to tree,

And at the root thro' lush green grasses burn'd

    The red anemone.

I knew the flowers, I knew the leaves, I knew

    The tearful glimmer of the languid dawn

On those long, rank, dark wood-walks drench'd in dew,

    Leading from lawn to lawn.

The smell of violets, hidden in the green,

    Pour'd back into my empty soul and frame

The times when I remember to have been

    Joyful and free from blame.

And from within me a clear under-tone

    Thrill'd thro' mine ears in that unblissful clime,

"Pass freely thro': the wood is all thine own,

    Until the end of time."

HELEN OF TROY.

At length I saw a lady within call,
 Stiller than chisell'd marble, standing there;
A daughter of the gods, divinely tall,
 And most divinely fair.

Her loveliness with shame and with surprise
 Froze my swift speech: she turning on my face
The star-like sorrows of immortal eyes,
 Spoke slowly in her place.

"I had great beauty: ask thou not my name:
 No one can be more wise than destiny.
Many drew swords and died. Where'er I came
 I brought calamity."

"No marvel, sovereign lady: in fair field
 Myself for such a face had boldly died,"

IPHIGENIA.

I answer'd free; and turning I appeal'd

　To one that stood beside.

But she, with sick and scornful looks averse,

　To her full height her stately stature draws;

"My youth," she said, "was blasted with a curse:

　This woman was the cause.

"I was cut off from hope in that sad place,

　Which yet to name my spirit loathes and fears:

My father held his hand upon his face;

　I, blinded with my tears,

"Still strove to speak: my voice was thick with sighs

　As in a dream. Dimly I could descry

The stern black-bearded kings with wolfish eyes,

　Waiting to see me die.

"The high masts flicker'd as they lay afloat;

   The crowds, the temples, waver'd, and the shore;

The bright death quiver'd at the victim's throat;

   Touch'd; and I knew no more."

Whereto the other with a downward brow:

  " I would the white cold heavy-plunging foam,

Whirl'd by the wind, had roll'd me deep below,

  Then when I left my home."

Her slow full words sank thro' the silence drear,

  As thunder-drops fall on a sleeping sea:

Sudden I heard a voice that cried, " Come here,

  That I may look on thee."

I turning saw, throned on a flowery rise,

    One sitting on a crimson scarf unroll'd;

A queen, with swarthy cheeks and bold black eyes,

    Brow-bound with burning gold.

CLEOPATRA.

She, flashing forth a haughty smile, began:

" I govern'd men by change, and so I sway'd

All moods. 'T is long since I have seen a man.

Once, like the moon, I made

" The ever-shifting currents of the blood

According to my humor ebb and flow.

I have no men to govern in this wood:

That makes my only woe.

" Nay — yet it chafes me that I could not bend

One will; nor tame and tutor with mine eye

That dull cold-blooded Cæsar. Prythee, friend,

Where is Mark Antony?

" The man, my lover, with whom I rode sublime

On Fortune's neck: we sat as God by God:

The Nilus would have risen before his time

    And flooded at our nod.

"We drank the Libyan sun to sleep, and lit

    Lamps which outburn'd Canopus. O my life

In Egypt! O the dalliance and the wit,

    The flattery and the strife,

"And the wild kiss, when fresh from war's alarms,
  My Hercules, my Roman Antony,
My mailed Bacchus leapt into my arms,
  Contented there to die!

"And there he died: and when I heard my name
  Sigh'd forth with life I would not brook my fear
Of the other: with a worm I balk'd his fame.
  What else was left? look here!"

(With that she tore her robe apart, and half
  The polish'd argent of her breast to sight
Laid bare. Thereto she pointed with a laugh,
  Showing the aspic's bite.)

"I died a Queen. The Roman soldier found
  Me lying dead, my crown about my brows,

A name forever! — lying robed and crown'd,
    Worthy a Roman spouse."

Her warbling voice, a lyre of widest range
    Struck by all passion, did fall down and glance
From tone to tone, and glided thro' all change
    Of liveliest utterance.

When she made pause I knew not for delight;
  Because with sudden motion from the ground
She raised her piercing orbs, and fill'd with light
  The interval of sound.

Still with their fires Love tipt his keenest darts;
  As once they drew into two burning rings
All beams of Love, melting the mighty hearts
  Of captains and of kings.

Slowly my sense undazzled. Then I heard
  A noise of some one coming thro' the lawn,
And singing clearer than the crested bird,
  That claps his wings at dawn.

"The torrent brooks of hallow'd Israel
  From craggy hollows pouring, late and soon,

Sound all night long, in falling thro' the dell,

Far-heard beneath the moon.

"The balmy moon of blessed Israel

Floods all the deep-blue gloom with beams divine:

All night the splinter'd crags that wall the dell

With spires of silver shine."

As one that museth where broad sunshine laves

The lawn by some cathedral, thro' the door

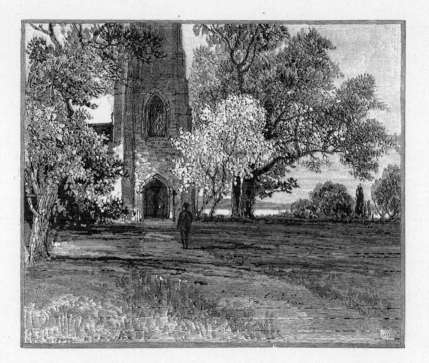

Hearing the holy organ rolling waves

Of sound on roof and floor

JEPHTHA'S DAUGHTER.

Within, and anthem sung, is charm'd and tied

    To where he stands, — so stood I, when that flow

Of music left the lips of her that died

    To save her father's vow;

The daughter of the warrior Gileadite,

    A maiden pure; as when she went along

From Mizpeh's tower'd gate with welcome light,

  With timbrel and with song.

My words leapt forth: "Heaven heads the count of crimes

  With that wild oath." She render'd answer high:

"Not so, nor once alone; a thousand times

  I would be born and die.

"Single I grew, like some green plant, whose root
    Creeps· to the garden water-pipes beneath,
Feeding the flower; but ere my flower to fruit
    Changed, I was ripe for death.

"My God, my land, my father, — these did move
    Me from my bliss of life, that Nature gave,
Lower'd softly with a threefold cord of love
    Down to a silent grave.

"And I went mourning, 'No fair Hebrew boy
    Shall smile away my maiden blame among
The Hebrew mothers' — emptied of all joy,
    Leaving the dance and song,

"Leaving the olive-gardens far below,
    Leaving the promise of my bridal bower,

The valleys of grape-loaded vines that glow

Beneath the battled tower.

" The light white cloud swam over us.   Anon

 We heard the lion roaring from his den;

We saw the large white stars rise one by one,

 Or, from the darken'd glen,

" Saw God divide the night with flying flame,

 And thunder on the everlasting hills.

I heard Him, for He spake, and grief became
    A solemn scorn of ills.

"When the next moon was roll'd into the sky,
    Strength came to me that equall'd my desire.
How beautiful a thing it was to die
    For God and for my sire!

"It comforts me in this one thought to dwell,
    That I subdued me to my father's will;
Because the kiss he gave me, ere I fell,
    Sweetens the spirit still.

"Moreover it is written that my race
    Hew'd Ammon, hip and thigh, from Aroer
On Arnon unto Minneth." Here her face
    Glow'd as I look'd at her.

She lock'd her lips: she left me where I stood:
"Glory to God," she sang, and past afar,

Thridding the sombre boskage of the wood,
Toward the morning-star.

Losing her carol I stood pensively,

    As one that from a casement leans his head,

When midnight bells cease ringing suddenly,

    And the old year is dead.

"Alas! alas!" a low voice, full of care,

    Murmur'd beside me: "Turn and look on me:

I am that Rosamond, whom men call fair,

    If what I was I be.

"Would I had been some maiden coarse and poor!

    O me, that I should ever see the light!

Those dragon eyes of anger'd Eleanor

    Do hunt me, day and night."

She ceased in tears, fallen from hope and trust:

    To whom the Egyptian: "O, you tamely died!

You should have clung to Fulvia's waist and thrust

    The dagger thro' her side."

With that sharp sound the white dawn's creeping beams,

    Stol'n to my brain, dissolved the mystery

MARGARET MORE.

Of folded sleep. The captain of my dreams

 Ruled in the eastern sky.

Morn broaden'd on the borders of the dark,

 Ere I saw her, who clasp'd in her last trance

Her murder'd father's head, or Joan of Arc,

 A light of ancient France;

JOAN OF ARC.

Or her, who knew that Love can vanquish Death,

Who kneeling, with one arm about her king,

Drew forth the poison with her balmy breath,

Sweet as new buds in Spring.

QUEEN ELEANOR.

No memory labors longer from the deep

    Gold-mines of thought to lift the hidden ore

That glimpses, moving up, than I from sleep

    To gather and tell o'er

Each little sound and sight. With what dull pain

    Compass'd, how eagerly I sought to strike

Into that wondrous track of dreams again!

    But no two dreams are like.

As when a soul laments, which hath been blest,

   Desiring what is mingled with past years,

In yearnings that can never be exprest

   By signs or groans or tears;

Because all words, tho' cull'd with choicest art,

   Failing to give the bitter of the sweet,

Wither beneath the palate, and the heart

   Faints, faded by its heat.